ALICIA KEYS
AS I AM

© International Music Publications Ltd
International Music Publications Ltd is a Faber Music company
3 Queen Square, London WC1N 3AU

Printed in USA

ISBN: 0-571-53172-5
EAN: 978-0-571-53172-1

To buy Faber Music pu̶̶̶̶̶̶̶̶̶̶̶̶̶ of titles available
please contact y̶̶̶̶̶̶̶̶̶̶̶̶̶̶̶̶̶̶̶̶̶̶̶̶̶ enquiries:

Faber Music Ltd.̶̶X England
Tel: +4̶̶̶̶̶̶̶̶̶̶̶̶̶̶̶̶̶̶̶̶̶̶̶̶̶̶̶̶̶
sales@fabermusic.com fabermusic.com

CONTENTS

AS I AM
(Intro)

Words and Music by
ALICIA KEYS

Slowly, very expressively

Moderately, steadily

GO AHEAD

Words and Music by ALICIA KEYS, KERRY BROTHERS, JR.,
MARK BATSON and MARSHA AMBROSIUS

Recorded a half step lower.

Am · Bm11 · Esus · Dsus2

lies, lies?) Go a-head, come on and get up

A/C♯ · Am/C · Esus · Dsus2

out-ta here, go a-head, ba - by. You knew you was wrong; you

A/C♯ · Am/C · Esus · Dsus2

knew all a-long, must be cra - zy. If you think I'm 'a fall for

A/C♯ · Am/C · Em · Dsus2

this an-y-more, ev-'ry-bod-y sing: (No, no,

SUPERWOMAN

Words and Music by ALICIA KEYS,
LINDA PERRY and STEVE MOSTYN

Ev - 'ry - where _ I'm turn - ing, ___

noth - ing seems _ com - plete.

can't be found, ___ I start to get weak, ___ 'cause

no one knows ___ me un-der-neath these clothes, ___ but

I can fly, ___

we can fly. ___ 'Cause

NO ONE

Words and Music by ALICIA KEYS,
KERRY BROTHERS, JR. and GEORGE HARRY

You __ and me to-geth-er _____ through the days and nights. ___

___ I don't wor-ry 'cause __ ev-'ry-thing's gon-na be al - right. __

Peo - ple keep __ talk-in', _____ they can say __ what they like. ___

But __ all I know __ is ev-'ry-thing's gon-na be al - right. _____ And no __ one, no __

LIKE YOU'LL NEVER SEE ME AGAIN

Words and Music by ALICIA KEYS
and KERRY BROTHERS, JR.

LESSON LEARNED

Words and Music by ALICIA KEYS,
RAPHAEL SAADIQ and JOHN MAYER

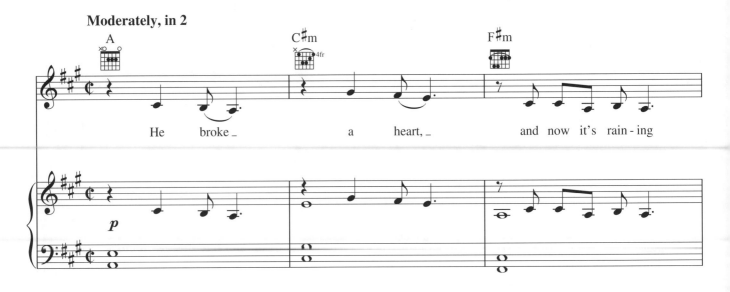

He broke _ a heart, _ and now it's rain-ing

just to rub it in.   I'm at ____ your door; _

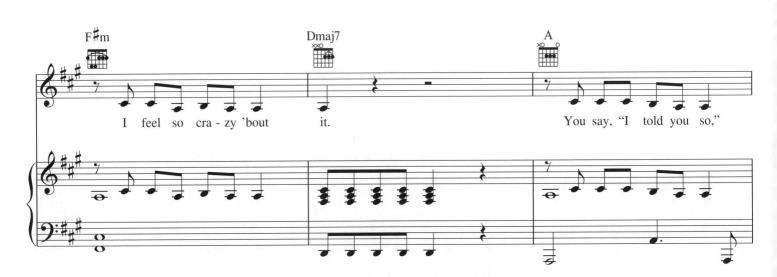

I feel so cra-zy 'bout it.   You say, "I told you so,"

E7sus
Bm11
an - oth - er les - son (learned). Life per - fect ain't per - fect if you don't
F♯m7
E(add4)
know what the strug - gle's for.
Bm11
F♯m7
Fall - ing down ain't fall - ing down if you don't cry when you hit the floor.
E(add4)
Bm11
It's called the past 'cause I'm get - tin' past and I ain't

WRECKLESS LOVE

Words and Music by ALICIA KEYS,
JACK SPLASH and HAROLD LILLY, JR.

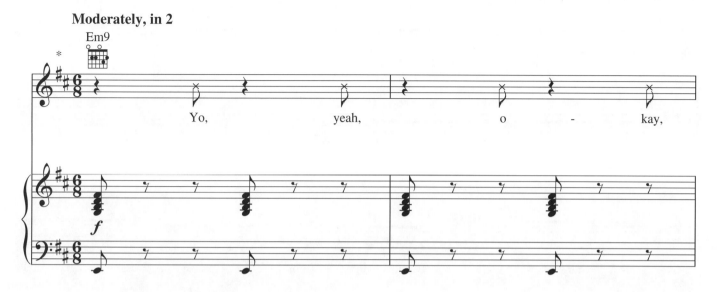

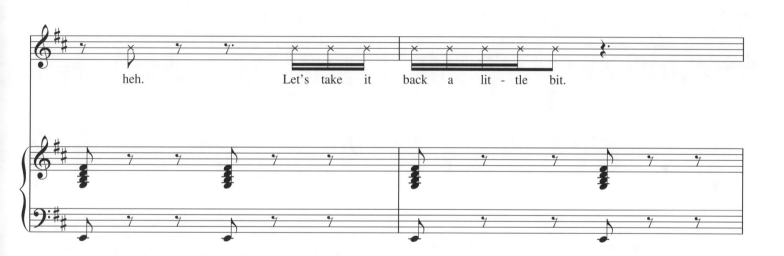

* Recorded a half step lower.

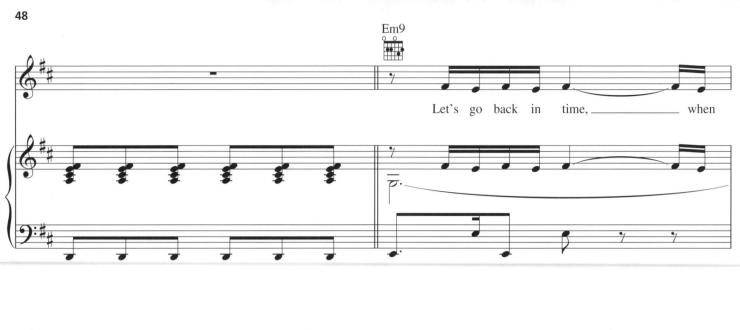

Let's go back in time, _____ when

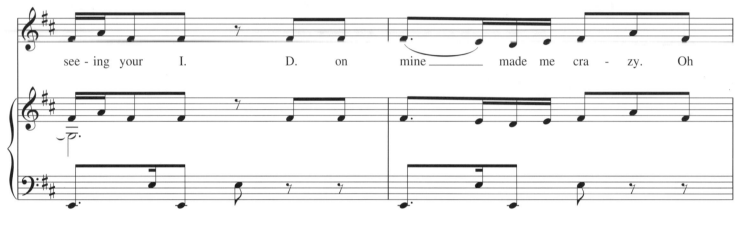

see - ing your I. D. on mine _____ made me cra - zy. Oh

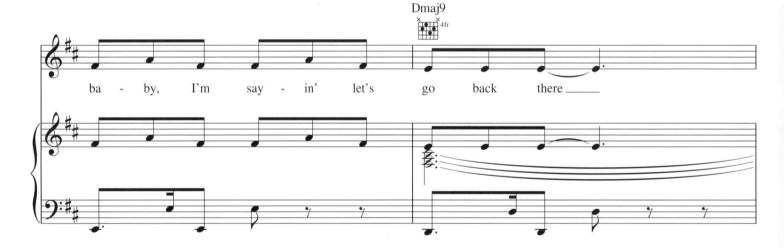

ba - by, I'm say - in' let's go back there _____

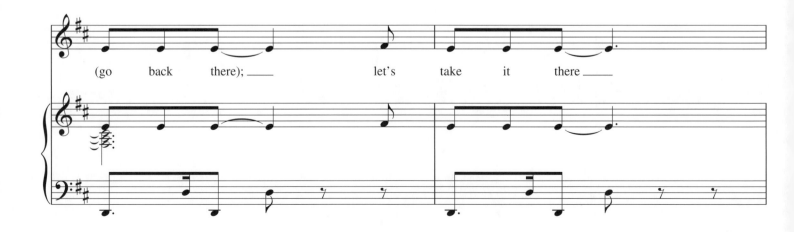

(go back there); _____ let's take it there _____

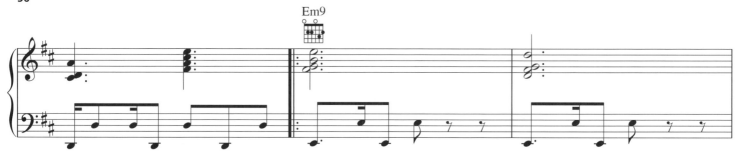

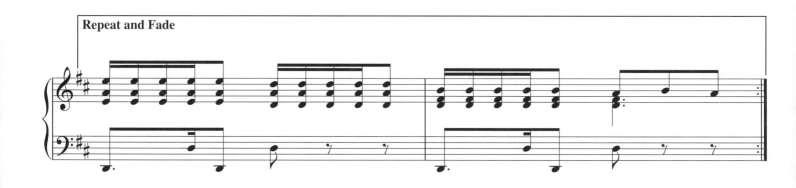

THE THING ABOUT LOVE

Words and Music by ALICIA KEYS
and LINDA PERRY

it's 'bout time _____ for me to

Slower, expressively

shine. _____

'Cause ev-'ry-bod-y laughs __ and ev-'ry-bod-y cries. ___

Sure, it could hurt you, ba - by, but give it a lit-tle try. ___

TEENAGE LOVE AFFAIR

Words and Music by ALICIA KEYS, JACK SPLASH,
HAROLD LILLY, JR., CARL HAMPTON,
JO BRIDGES and and TOM NIXON

Recorded a half step lower.

It's a mat-ter of ex-treme im-por-tance, my first teen-age love af-fair, baby, ba-by. teen-age love af-fair.

I NEED YOU

Words and Music by ALICIA KEYS, PAUL GREEN,
HAROLD LILLY, JR. and MARK BATSON

the sky can't wait

for the light of the sun.

So how could you

look me in my eye and not see what,

WHERE DO WE GO FROM HERE

Words and Music by ALICIA KEYS,
KERRY BROTHERS, JR., HAROLD LILLY, JR.,
JOSEPH FRIERSON and MARY FRIERSON

PRELUDE TO A KISS

Words and Music by
ALICIA KEYS

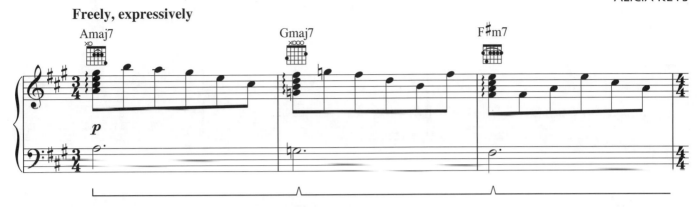

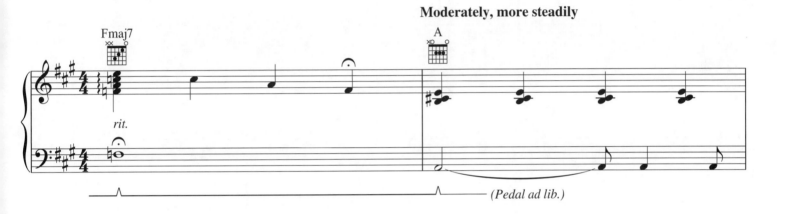

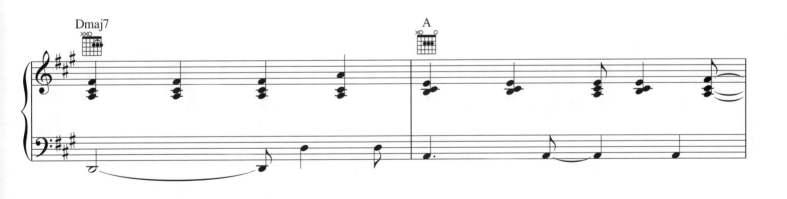

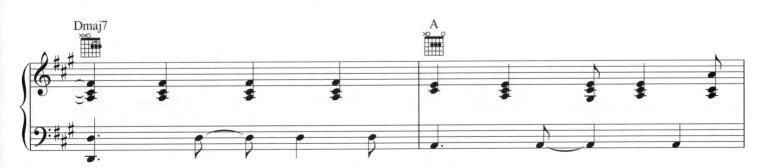

an - gel _____ to guide _____

_____ me? _____

Repeat ad lib. and Fade

Optional Ending

TELL YOU SOMETHING
(Nana's Reprise)

Words and Music by ALICIA KEYS, KERRY BROTHERS, JR.,
ALONZO STEVENSON, PAUL GREEN,
RAY HANEY and STEVE MOSTYN

I can't wait, _ I can't wait, _ I won't wait, _ I don't wan-

na wait.

I can't wait, _ I can't wait, _

_ I won't wait, _ I don't wan - na wait.

Optional Ending

Repeat and Fade

SURE LOOKS GOOD TO ME

Words and Music by ALICIA KEYS
and LINDA PERRY